LIGHT
IN THE DARKNESS

SELECTED STORIES

by

M. D, WEINSTOCK

Translated by Kathleen Szász
Illustrated by Emmanuil Snitkovsky

Printed in U.S.

BEZALEL ART, 11 Essex Street, New York, N.Y. 10002
5742/ 1982

CONTENTS

Paperback   ISBN 0-914734-03-2

Library of Congress Cat. No. 72-86118

FOREWORD

It is with a profound sense of unworthiness that I have accepted the privilege of introducing these stories to English readers. They reflect the heights of holiness to which our martyred brethren could ascend through the very depths of fiendish cruelty inflicted upon them; and their overpowering impression of holiness defying the enemies of God, merits a more eloquent introduction than any that I can offer.

The author is the editor of an orthodox weekly in Hungarian in the Holy City. In our day and age, only Hungarian Jewry could have produced a phenomenon such as he and his readers constitute. Testifying as he does through both outward and inward manifestations to his strong intimate attachment to the sacred way of life and thought propagated by the holy Baal Shem and his holy disciples, he yet has the capacity to write with distinction in the language of the country of his origin for the benefit of those who share his religious sentiments and his mother-tongue. The result is deeply moving. Unlike secularist writers who have described experiences in the camps of extermination, our author prefers to dwell on the spiritual aspects of suffering and martyrdom for the sanctification of the Holy Name, on the readiness for self-sacrifice in obedience to the decree from Above and on obedience to the commandments of the Holy Torah in the valley of the shadow itself.

My tears, I must confess, made many large smudges on the copy of the manuscript entrusted to me. The dramatic element in these tales, the sense of the divine drama in which human beings are involved, and given a measure of freedom for the shaping of their own roles, made me read on eagerly to the end. For this is no record of atrocities but an account of spiritual adventures through which our faith can derive strength and our resolve to draw nearer to our Creator through the meticulous performance of His orders be fortified. The hope that through these tales of exalted martyrdom, believers will be led to higher levels of precept and practice and that those who have lost their way, will be restored to the right path, has prompted me to recommend this book.

Emile Marmorstein.

ABRAHAM'S COVENANT

RABBI Shapira, Rabbi of Prachnik, grandson of the holy Zadik of Bluzhov, was sawing a huge log with his weak hands in the midst of the forest of Janow, to which place the Jews from the ghetto had been herded for forest clearing. He sawed the wood with twisted hands, emaciated arms, his body racked with hunger, to perform a task of "vital importance" in aid of the great victory of the glorious Wehrmacht over its inferior enemy.

The keen mind of the Rabbi of Prachnik, polished to perfection on the Talmud, was not functioning as faultlessly as would befit one of his genius. The saw, cutting deep into the great log, creaked agonisingly, and pain drove every thought from Rabbi Shapira's mind. It seemed to him as if flames of torment were whirling round in his head. Even his memories deserted him in the depths of this forest where the rifle-butts of the S.S. torturers had driven him. Who can picture the state of mind of a galley-slave, the hopeless apathy, in which the sufferer no longer remembers the past and no longer believes in the reality of the world? The atmosphere was leaden and as heavy as if it had been crowded with evil black shadows; and only seldom could a stray thought enter the mind, the bitter product of constant apathy and grief.

Thousands of victims had been brought to the camp that day, among them many young mothers with infants in their arms, curly headed babes whose hair had never known scissors. The older ones, the four and five year olds, played thoughtlessly in the shadow of death; but the mothers, who realized that they had born their children for the lime-pit, sat for hours on end, motionless, unutterable misery in their eyes.

"What a devilish, foul crime" the thought preyed on Rabbi Shapira's tortured mind — "to murder these innocent little children."

The saw ate its way groaning into the log when Rabbi Shapira heard steps approaching behind his back. Involuntarily, he worked faster, because he was certain that an S.S. man was standing behind him. He glanced over his shoulder and to his amazement he saw a young Jewish mother with a little baby in her arm. How had this unfortunate, condemned woman got into the forest of Janow? How had she managed to come so far from the camp?

Was she trying to escape? But the whole area was swarming with kapos and S.S.-men! She could not even get a hundred yards from here!

But no, this unhappy young woman, betrothed to death, was not trying to escape. On the contrary, she was coming towards him, seeking him.

"Have you a knife? Give it to me quickly, I beg you" she whispered, a wild defiance blazing in her eyes.

"A knife? For what purpose?" the prisoner asked in alarm, the prisoner who had once been the Rabbi of Prachnik.

"A knife!" she repeated over and over again, almost stubbornly, and he felt a strange resistance rising in his heart.

"Don't throw away your life, wait for your time to come. Perhaps before two hours are past, you shall share in the most exalted Jewish fate and die the death of a martyr. You shall die because your fathers, your forefathers, cherished an unshakable belief in the triumph of a pure and ethical life. Centuries, thousands of years ago, they could have chosen the cruel, foolish way of life followed by other peoples, but they obeyed the Will of the Creator Who conceived the thought of placing souls upon this earth, who represent the heavenly attributes

of goodness and justice, and spread light throughout the world. For this special task, he found a race
which replied 'Naaseh venishma', we will accept
the yoke, we will shoulder it unconditionally. Then
Satan, angered by such boldness, resolved to fight
this people, Israel. When at the time of the Cossack-
revolt in 1648, the blood of a hundred thousand
Jews drenched the soil, the saintly Reb Samson
Ostropoler spoke to Satan:

"Listen, Satan, why do you not fight another
people, why do you always persecute unfortunate
Israel?"

Satan's face broke into a truly devilish grin as he
replied:

"I am willing to do so. Just give up to me the
Sabbath and the commandment of circumcision, and
you will be free from me!"

"No, and a thousand times no," proclaimed Reb
Samson. "Let millions and millions die, we shall
never depart one iota from the Commandments of
the Torah." So you see now, you who have been
elected to martyrdom, of what noble stock you are a
descendant? And you want to deprive yourself now
of the merit of martyrdom before its consummation?"

No sooner had he concluded his explanation of
the sin of suicide to the desperate Jewish woman,

than he heard with consternation the sound of heavy S.S. boots behind him.

"Du Schwein! Du Hund" the S.S. man shouted, beside himself with rage, and struck the Rabbi with his heavy fist. "Don't you know it is forbidden to speak to prisoners? Were you two conspiring against us?" he roared and hit the Rabbi again and again.

"No, Sir, this unfortunate woman asked me for a knife, obviously with the intention of killing herself, and I did all in my power to dissuade her. I did not want her to lose her salvation by committing such a grave sin.

The Nazi stopped his blows and looked incredulously at the rabbi who had fallen to the ground.

"What strange, fanatical people you are."

Lowering his voice, he turned to the trembling woman who pressed her child protectively to her bosom.

"Is it true what this Jew is saying?"

"It is the absolute truth" replied the woman. The fire blazing in her eyes seemed to drive sorrow from her face. "It is true that I asked this man for a knife, but I did not intend to kill myself with it. I needed it for another purpose."

"What purpose?"

The woman straightened up, radiating self-assurance and an almost transcendent pride.

"We Jews have a Law," she said in a low but unhesitating voice, "that all male children are to be admitted into Abraham's Covenant. My little boy has not yet been circumcised. That was why I asked for a knife.

The pagan brute who was perhaps a village school-master in civilian life, and taught German children the superiority of materialism, could hardly conceive that a downtrodden, wretched woman, condemned to death, should possess such fortitude. However, he did not want to seem sentimental.

"Idiotic fanaticism" he murmured.

"My child is a Jewish child. He was born a Jew, and I want to return him to his Creator circumcised, in accordance with His Command.

"I don't believe it." said the S.S. man. Then obeying a sudden impulse, he drew the bayonet and handed it to the woman with a cynical smile:

"Here, perhaps this will do for your purpose."

And the young Jewish woman stood in the middle of the forest of Janow, on the autumnal soil of a strange, accursed land, as if she had stepped out of the pages of the Midrash. She made the necessary preparations, then fervently recited the benediction:

and using the bayonet as a knife, circumcised her son.

"Amen" the rabbi responded to the blessing and his face, too, was transfigured with joy.

'Amen" replied the Ministering Angels, and the ancestors, the great Jewish minds of all times. In that moment, the Jewish genius shone with a strength intensified a millionfold in the heavenly world.

"A Jewish Mother has once more saved the honour of mankind," proclaimed a Heavenly Voice and a tear sparkled in the Eye of the Creator.

THE GERMAN COLONEL

COLD autumn winds were blowing when the train carrying the Rabbi of Zhabne and his retinue ran into the railway station of the famous Bavarian spa of W. The medium-sized traveller with his silvery beard and shining eyes, got off the train carefully, walking with a slight limp. The Gabe, a fragile, bespectacled little man, hurried ahead to find a carriage. The Rabbi of Zhabne followed more slowly, leaning on the arm of his son-in-law, the tall and majestic Rabbi of Prachnik.

The few people loitering around the station-building gazed at the imposing strangers with unconcealed awe.

"Wonder-working rabbis from Poland." they whispered among themselves.

The landlord of the "pension" where they descended received them like old acquaintances. The Rabbi of Zhabne had taken the cure the year before and, because it had done him a great deal of good, his physicians advised him to return again to the medicinal springs of W. There was no other spa like W. in the whole of Europe.

"Sholem aleichem," the landlord, Herr Hermann, a German Jew, greeted his guests with a broad smile. "Welcome to my distinguished visitors." And with that he conducted them to the tastefully furnished and spotlessly clean rooms that had been prepared for them where the newcomers soon felt completely at home.

November was the depth of the quiet season, and the resort was but sparsely populated. Yet, in the afternoons, when the two rabbis set out for their usual walk, many a man inclined his head in respectful greeting. They were well remembered from the previous year when they had spent two months at W. Both men were of conspicuously distinguished appearance and princely gait, their faces reflected nobility, intelligence and kindliness. Whoever met them fell under their spell.

One evening, after the maariv prayer, Herr Hermann, the landlord came knocking at their door.

"You have been done a great honour, my dear guests," he began, "a very highranking state official staying at the neighbouring villa has expressed a desire to make your acquaintance.

The Rabbi of Zhabne made a gesture of refusal.

"Don't decline the invitation, I beg of you" Herr Hermann pressed them, "who knows whether this high connection will not, one day, be of advantage to you. . ."

The next day a fairheaded, blue-eyed German of some thirty-five years of age presented himself at the "pension".

"My name is Oscar Muller, from Dusseldorf" he introduced himself. "I have heard of your great wisdom and, being a religious man myself, and one deeply interested in religious philosophy, I should consider it an honour if you would accept my company."

Day after day the son-in-law of the Rabbi of Zhabne, Rabbi Shapira, spent hours of his time trying to satisfy the inexhaustable curiosity of the young German, who introduced every new question by saying: "Please, enlighten me. . . "

Sometimes Oscar Muller's thirst for knowledge grew most irksome. After all, the two rabbis had not come to W. to listen to the chatter of an eccentric German, but to take the cure and, withdrawing into solitude, to lose themselves in the study of the Torah. During their afternoon walks in the park of the resort, Oscar Muller hung on their every word with almost fanatical adoration. He often said he felt as inferior to these great scholars as a dwarf in the company of giants.

Even so, in the course of time, a certain friendship developed between the two rabbis and the German. Every year, Oscar Muller sent them his good wishes on the occasion of the Jewish New Year and the rabbis repaid him for his attention by sending him their greetings on the occasion of the secular New Year. Oscar Muller arranged his annual holiday in a way that would enable him to join his two friends at the resort of W., usually at the end of November.

"He is a decent, intelligent man, this Oscar Muller." the Rabbi of Zhabne said one day, and yet, I have a strange feeling when we are in his company."

It was then the year 1928.

Eleven years went by, and storm clouds were gathering over the heads of the Jews of Poland. Hitler's hordes overran their country. No Polish Jew was safe from the Nazis. A wave of persecution and murder swept across the country. Wherever the Nazis went, precious Jewish blood was shed until few drops of it remained in the great reservoir of our people. The unfortunate victims were driven into ghettos and subsequently exterminated.

Rabbi Shapira of Prachnik was deported to one of the worst concentration camps in Poland, the camp of Janow. The inmates of the camp, Jewish-slave-labourers, were herded out day after day to build a railway line. They were emaciated beyond recognition and only by the greatest effort could they still move their limbs. Each day hundreds succumbed to sickness and starvation. The angel of death reaped a rich harvest in this camp.

The once powerful Rabbi of Prachnik lifted heavy rails only by the greatest exertion of his will power. The last two days had been difficult beyond imagination. The S.S. men had constantly beaten and tormented their prisoners, the hunger was unbearable. The rabbi felt that very soon his strength would fail him. He raised his head and noticed a civilian approaching their line.

Who is this stranger?" he turned to his neighbour. "How is it possible that they let him come so near to us?"

"The men wearing civilian clothes are foreign Jews, foreign nationals" the man replied. "They live beyond the level crossing. Their lot is incomparably better than our, they don't have to work and are permitted to walk around for two or three hours each day. The man coming toward us is a physician from Greiditz."

"From Greiditz?" Rabbi Shapira said surprised. "I lived at Greiditz for four years."

When the civilian reached their lines, Rabbi Shapira lowered his voice to a whisper.

"Are you the doctor from Greiditz?"

"Yes."

"Did you know Rabbi Shapira of Prachnik?"

"Of course, I knew him. He was a great scholar and a wise man. They say he was liquidated in the ghetto. It is a real tragedy, for he was an extraordinary man. I often attended his Beth Hamidrash while he was at Greiditz. . ."

"And if I were to tell you that Rabbi Shapira is alive," the Rabbi of Prachnik asked, "would you help him?"

"I should gladly give my life for him," the doctor replied with deep conviction.

For a minute there was silence, the rabbi gazed down upon his heavy wodden clogs.

Then he said quietly: "I am Rabbi Shapira."

"Good heavens!" the doctor exclaimed in amazement. "You, in this condition. . . I should never have recognized you! But this is not the time to wonder and hesitate, this is the time to act. You must get out of here! I shall smuggle you into our camp. Only boldness will be of avail. Either we succeed, or we both perish."

Quickly the doctor took off his overcoat.

"Put this on" he told the rabbi.

Then he took off his cap and passed that too to the rabbi.

"This is fine" he said satisfied, "now take your courage into both hands follow me."

The S.S. guard at the level crossing acknowledged the greeting of the doctor whom he knew by sight from having seen him walk that way before, then turned away whistling. The Rabbi of Prachnik reached the camp of the foreign Jews.

For the first time in two years he saw a bed, a table, relatively human conditions. His new friends plied him with food and drink, but his weakened organism could no longer accept nourishment. His strength left him, he fainted. It took several days before he was able to eat properly.

The "foreign" Jews in the camp were mainly from Galicia and knew the fame of the Rabbi of Prachnik, grandson of the Zadik of Bluzhov. They put their heads together and conferred for hours to find some way to help him. The problem was not easy to solve: Only Jews possessing foreign passports were permitted to remain in this camp. Now, Rabbi Shapira owned a document certifying that he was the citizen of a South-American state, that had been purchased for a great deal of money at the beginning of those chaotic times, but unfortunately that document was buried, together with some treasured and highly valuable objects, at Prachnik. How were they to lay hands on it?

There was but one solution. Sasha, a cheerful and exeedingly willing young man who looked truly Aryan, was able to travel freely throughout the country. He must be entrusted with the task of finding the document.

"Yes, but it is buried in the mayor's garden and the mayor hates Jews" said the rabbi.

"Let him have the treasure, then, and you get the document" his friends advised.

Sasha immediately declared himself ready to go after the document. He soon returned with it, though no one ever found out how he managed it. The "foreign" Jews and Rabbi Shapira were beside themselves with joy.

Naturally the possession of such a document did not offer a guarantee of safety. Every four weeks an S.S. Colonel arrived at the camp to examine the papers of the "foreigners". Sometimes he altered the date of expiration, but sometimes he "discovered" some formal mistake — and already he had pressed the button.

What did pressing the button mean? It meant death. The end. When the Colonel pressed the button, two devils in S.S. uniform decorated with a death's head rushed into the room, grasped the unfortunate victim and carried him off. The rifle shot heard from the cellar left no doubt as to the fate of the man whose papers the Colonel had invalidated.

The fateful day arrived, the Colonel drove into the camp. Rabbi Shapira felt that his last day had come. There was no escape. The inmates of the camp lined up and waited, trembling in dread of what was to come. Rabbi Shapira withdrew more and more into the background as if to delay the dreaded moment.

With dragging feet, as if his limbs were of lead, he set out toward the Colonel's office. But as he entered the anteroom, his eyes strayed to the name-plate on the door. "Oberst Oscar Muller" — was what he read.

Where had he heard that name before? But there was no time to think. The Colonel stood before him. He was a tall, greyhaired man, his face seemed familiar to the rabbi. But no, that couldn't be! The

Oscar Muller he once knew was a mild, decent man his deceased father-in-law, the Rabbi of Zhabne had always said : "A German like this is a rarity!" This Oscar Muller, however, looked like a beast of prey.

"Du Sau! Du Schwein!" the Colonel roared like a madman. "Where did you steal this document?" Not waiting for an answer he threw the paper into the rabbi's face. The rabbi recoiled, half conscious, but he still saw the Colonel press the button. With a desperate effort, he jumped forward.

"Give me a minute, only one minute, Colonel! Are you not Oscar Muller from Dusseldorf?"

"I am" the Colonel replied involuntarily.

"Don't you remember me? I am Rabbi Shapira."

The Colonel threw up his hands, gasping in astonishment.

"Are you really my excellent friend, the Rabbi of Prachnik? How could I have recognized you?"

His face underwent an amazing change, the evil lines seemed to disappear, he looked younger, milder. Rabbi Shapira's companion on many walks at the resort of W. was again the gentleman he had once been.

"Sit down, my dear rabbi, and tell me about yourself. How is your distinguished father-in-law?"

"He has been dead for a long time."

"What a wise man and great scholar he was! What sparkling wit! What conversation. . . And your wife and little daughter, where are they?"

Rabbi Shapira sat as if petrified, then suddenly he broke into heartrending sobs. For years he had been unable to cry, as if all his tears had been spent, but now he was shaking from head to foot under the onslaught of a terrible emotion.

"Calm yourself, calm yourself, my dear rabbi," the Colonel begged him "you are safe now. Your safety will be my personal responsibility!"

Then he reached for the telephone and called his wife.

"If you only knew, my dear Lotte, who is here with me at this moment" He smiled sweetly into the receiver. "No, you'll never guess. It is our old friend, Rabbi Shapira! You remember him, don't you? Join me at once and bring some fruit and good food with you!"

Soon the Colonel's wife arrived, her basket brimming with delicacies.

"The good rabbi must have a room of his own," she commanded and went off to select the best room and furnish it herself. Even a free man might have envied the rabbi for all the attention devoted to him.

After a little while, the rabbi asked the Colonel to

allow him to share his room with a few others on the grounds that it was not good for a man to live alone. The Colonel agreed and thus Rabbi Shapira was able to help some of his closest friends. A veritable "golden age" followed, Rabbi Shapira felt that he had witnessed a miracle like that shown to the Joseph Ha-Zadik in his dungeon.

Let no one believe, however, that Oberst Oscar Muller was changed by his meeting with his old friend. The presence of the "esteemed rabbi" did not influence him in the least. He remained the same cold and ruthless murderer he had been before. By pressing down the little button, he still sent Jews to their deaths. But Rabbi Shapira was different! Rabbi Shapira was his own favourite friend. He would have done anything for Rabbi Shapira.

Who can plunge to the depth of that tinfoil-lined sewer, the German psyche?

For a year and a half, Rabbi Shapira enjoyed the protection of Oberst Oscar Muller who, at one time, saved him and fifteen of his friends from extermination; and, later, when the Rabbi of Prachnik was moved to Bergen-Belsen, the Colonel wrote a letter of recommendation to the S.S. commander of the camp, asking him to favour the rabbi with his good graces.

BEN ZION

THE people asked themselves: "What has happened to our Benzion? He has always been our pride, an example to our children, what could have caused this change in him?"

Benzion was the son of the richest man in our town, Amrom Reichenthal. In addition to his coal and timber business, he owned fertile fields and extensive forests on the slopes of the Tatra Mountains. Benzion had been brought up in the yeshiva of Hannusfalva where he was the favourite of the rabbi. He excelled not only by virtue of his diligence, but also through his razor-sharp mind. He was quick in his grasp of essentials as well as in rejection of the inessential. His character matched his brilliance and he was beloved by all for the gentleness of his nature, for his good heart and his readiness to help others. Everyone in the yeshiva looked up to him as to a shining example. He spent every Thursday night in study, and on Friday night, after the rabbi had risen from the festive table, he led the proceedings and maintained the festive mood. Later in the evening, when the "balebatim" of the little town were fast asleep, melodies soared from his throat, as loftily as if they had been borne on the wings of an eagle. "Words of Torah" alternated with the traditional songs, the Tatra mountains echoed them and constituted a fascinating background for them until it seemed as if the mountains themselves shared in the singers' fervour when the haunting melody of the *"meain oilom habo"* rose into the nightly air.

In later years, when he no longer studied in the yeshiva, he always arranged to meet his rabbi at the time when he was accustomed to spending part of the summer with his pupils in the Tatra. They were unforgettable, those walks through the rich, billowing, yellow-green fields, the flowery meadows, the pine-groves where their songs broke the silence of the woods. The perfect harmony of the landscape attuned itself to the wonderful story of the Baal Shem, like a stream gushing forth from under a rock. Oh, happy, unforgettable youth! At the time, Benzion was earning his living by working in his father's business, but he still had plenty of leisure for study and for a *mizve* if anyone required help. How proud

his parents were of such a son, how they hung upon
his words!

And then suddenly came this great change!. . .
In the past Benzion had never neglected his studies,
but now, every Sunday, he put on his skis and went
out, early at dawn, into the mountains only to return
late in the night. He behaved as if he had never
read a book, he did not even participate in the in-
tonation of the Psalms, although, in view of the
troubled times, the rabbi of the small town insisted
on them being recited regularly. These were the
days of Hitler's conquests. Everyone knew what was
happening in the neighbouring countries and took
refuge in prayer. It seemed to be at such a time
that Benzion deserted us, that he permitted himself
to be misled by the evil inclination.

"Hide, seek shelter!" was the order of the day.
Hide, if possible, with the help of Christian acquaintances. Some succeeded in doing so, but there were
others who found nowhere to hide.

One morning, early, came a knock at the doors.

"Quick, hurry up, go to your hiding places. Within an hour the angel of destruction will be upon us"
someone called from outside. His trembling voice
betrayed his fear. A profound dread gripped all their

hearts. They packed a few belongings, dressed in haste, but the voice from outside bade them hurry:

"Those who have no place to hide and cannot go to shelters, should hurry from the town and wait at the edge of the forest!"

They breathed with relief, the Creator would not forsake them. Hurrying through dark alyways, they arrived at the appointed place where two trucks were waiting for them. They clambered in, and immediately the trucks started off with them, along the steep serpentine roads up the mountain side.

At five o'clock in the morning, the Hlinka guardists and the German S.S. appeared in the town but found not a single soul in the Jewish houses. In their fury they destroyed all the furniture.

The hiding place to which Benzion took the refugees was not easy to find. It was far from any human habitation, in a deep valley surrounded by high mountain peaks. A narrow path led down among steep cliffs. The path was hardly visible and, after a while, it disappeared altogether in the underbrush and nobody could guess that it led all the way down to the valley. The rock walls protected it like a fortress.

At the bottom of the valley two large wooden huts awaited the newcomers. Benzion and his friends had built them during the last few months. They had brought down the building material and the necessary tools on Sundays, on their skis in the greatest secrecy. Benzion had sensed the approaching danger and he had prepared for it. Now the time to act had arrived. He had forgotten nothing. There were not only tables, chairs, straw-mattresses, but he had even supplied toys for the children. The Sefer Torah and Seforim were naturally prepared. At the bottom of the valley, a crystal-clear streamlet supplied water. The state of mind of the persecuted people became calmer, their dreadful fears abated. They were filled with deep gratitude toward Benzion. They were also a little ashamed, how could they ever have believed that the evil inclination had lured him away? Now they knew that all the time he had been busy ensuring the safety of the Jewish population of the little town.

By means of considerable bribes, he had established contact with the S.S. in order to obtain information as to when the danger would threaten them, and thus, thanks to the Creator, not a single Jew fell into the hands of the knaves.

Gradually, they settled down in their new surroundings. The soil around the encampment was cultivated, the vegetable gardens were kept free from weeds and yielded a rich harvest. To their greatest surprise they also found two goats when they arrived and thus their food supply was fully ensured. Fresh vegetables and milk, what else was needed in those difficult days? They started the day with the morning prayer, after using the hastily rigged-up mikva. After that came work in the "fields" and after work, they assembled again for study.

Some fifty people lived in the two barracks, men, women, children, and each day they thanked the Lord for having protected them.

From time to time Benzion disappeared for a few days, after which he re-appeared again, nobody knew from where. It was rumoured among the encampment-dwellers that during his absences Benzion was going about in an S.S. uniform, that he changed his clothes when he returned, in a nearby cave. There were those who shook their heads in doubt, but others so deeply respected Benzion that they were convinced of his extraordinary courage. Weeks, months went by and the Jews lived in their deep valley cut off from the world outside. On his return from his mysterious trips, Benzion brought news of the allied victories and they waited, full of confidence, for their liberation.

Pesach was approaching. They selected wheat grains, and ground them in a little hand-mill. While they worked, the sounds of the Hallel rose from their lips. Not even at home could they have prepared more worthily for the coming feast or more in accordance with the rules. The women brightened up their everyday dresses and scrubbed the children clean. One of the huts was transformed into a dining room : the long table, spread with a white cloth, was decorated with flowers and even a few silver chalices appeared from the depths of rucksacks. They were full of hope as they sat at the seder and sang the familiar sacred melodies. They thought with faith in their hearts, that next year they would celebrate Pesach "beare de'Yisroel".

Benzion recited the Hagada with them and added comments. Now and again, he arose all of a sudden, as if anxious to make sure that the doors were properly locked. When he returned to the table, he was besieged on all sides with requests that he should speak. In vain did he protest, he had to satisfy their desire.

"According to our Sages, one should say as much as possible about the Exodus from Egypt. 'Kol hamarbe lesaper hare ze meshibach.' In this way Benzion began his address. "Ecclesiastes, on the other hand, says: 'There is a time for silence and there is a time for action'. In the explanation of the verse 'Why do you call to me? Speak to the children of Israel that they should journey,' the holy Or Ha'-chayim asked: 'And when should we call, when should we pray if not in the fateful hour? To whom? To the Creator. But there is also a time for action. Throw yourselves into the sea, according to the commandment, and Israel will be saved. My friends, let us pledge ourselves at this moment to sacrifice our lives for the Creator. Our pledge will also hasten the salvation of Klal Jisroel. We cannot know who will be saved, but it is certain that universal Jewry will survive. It is our purpose to preserve the whole of Israel for the future, because we all belong to the army of the Messiah. 'And truth springs from the good will of the just'. We must express our thanks to our rabbi, because we all owe it to him that we have found this sanctuary. Once, when we,, his disciples, met the Master on the occasion of one of his visits to the Tatra, he said to us: 'My sons, always remember the narrow mountain path on which we once walked. That path leads down to the valley, remember that when the time comes". We accepted this as a warning for the future and that is how we found this place. May his merits shield us."

After the address, those present heartily cheered Benzion and afterwards continued the seder until dawn. They were already reciting the Song of Songs, when suddenly the door was pushed open.

Their hearts seemed to stop beating. Two tough, savage-faced S.S. soldiers stood in the doorway with their guns pointed towards them. Instinctively, they all retreated to a corner of the hut.

The S.S. men showered them with crude, coarse and offensive words.

"You dirty Jewish swine, at last we have found you! It took long enough, but you will soon smell the flowers from below. Who is your leader?"

In the deadly silence, Benzion stepped forward.

"So it is you, you dog?" — and they struck him in the face.

Benzion stood straight with compressed lips.

"Now show us your little empire! You have made it comfortable enough for yourselves, a really re-markable effort! Come on!"

Benzion led them through the two huts and then they reached the small hut that stood in the middle of the kitchen garden. The population of the little settlement had always been forbidden to enter it. but only now did they find out why.

The moment that Benzion and the two S.S. men entered the hut, a most terrible explosion shattered the silence and the entire hut rose into the air. It had been undermined with ecrasite. The two S.S. soldiers perished and Benzion perished with them. We were saved. He had given his life to save ours.

A few days later the Russians arrived and we were liberated.

THE LAST MINUTE

ONCE every month Pinchas Kohn of Pittsburg pays a visit to the Rabbi of Prachnik, grandson of the famous Rabbi of Bluzhov. Rabbi Shapira of Prachnik is today one of the leading figures among the religious Jews of Brooklyn. His followers regard him as the spiritual heir of the famous Rabbis of the great dinasty of Dinov, and when they are near him, they re-live in their memories the wonderful times when they had flourished, when those almost superhuman beings, Rabbi Zwi Elimelech, the Rabbi of Dinov, and author of 'Bne Yisoschor' with its cabbalistic depth, and the Rabbi of Bluzhov, had attracted veritable processions of people wherever they went.

Only a miracle had saved the Rabbi of Prachnik from sharing the martyrdom of his brethren at the very outset of the terrible tragedy that befell the Jewish people of Poland. Tens of thousands moved forward on the road to death, like sheep to the slaughter-house, and among them was Rabbi Shapira, his wife and his highly gifted only daughter. They marched in silence, uncomplaining, certain that they would never return the same way.

The nazis were in need of workers. They selected men under the age of 45 and ordered them to a terrible place, the scene of mass murders. They were lined up for this work. Rabbi Shapira, although he was only 43, did not come forward. He waited, apathetically, for his fate to be fullfilled; but his wife called to one of the nazi henchmen sanding nearby:

"My husband isn't 45 yet."

The nazi examined the rabbi with malevolent eyes.

"How old are you, Jew?"

"Fifty five," the rabbi replied calmly.

"You want to perish with your family, don't you, Jew?" the nazi roared at him, and in his rage, struck the rabbi in the face. The rabbi fell to the ground, bleeding.

"The time for that hasn't come for you!" the nazi yelled, hurling the rabbi toward the group of selected workers.

Tens of thousands perished around him but, as if a powerful angel were standing beside him, protecting him from the sweeping scythe of death, he remained alive. Nobody could doubt the presence of an angel because no human imagination could

fathom how else a man could have survived the indescribable horrors among which he lived day after
day; but the Will of the Creator and the great merits
of his ancestors protected him like a coat of mail.
Death's scythe reaped before him and reaped behind
him, but he remained untouched.

His Brooklyn chasidim and their children — most-
of them born in America — listened with awe when
the rabbi related to them his experiences in the extermination camp. When Pinchas Kohn of Pittsburg
paid his first visit, Rabbi Shapira received him
with open arms and the greatest respect. To explain
his behaviour he turned to his chasidim, who were
hanging thirstily on his lips and told them the
following story:

"Do not be surprised that I receive Pinchas Kohn
with such deep joy. This is the least I can do. After
all, it was Mr.Kohn who, with the help of the Creator, saved my life."

The German beast, bleeding from a hundred
wounds, was writhing in the throes of death. The
Russians had surrounded Berlin and the allies in
their advance from the south-west toward the north,
were being held up only by minor skirmishes.

In Rabbi Shapira's camp the mortality rate had

reached its peak. As a result of the constant "selections" only 2800 prisoners were still alive in that sector of Bergen-Belsen camp. The more their hope of salvation grew, the more the prisoners grew afraid of death. Small wonder! The news that the allies were approaching could, at any moment, have prompted the beasts in whose hands they were, to revenge themselves on their helpless victims.

Their fear proved well founded. One day they were driven to the railway station and loaded into cattle-trucks. The S.S. were even more brutal than usual. Over a hundred people were crowded into each truck. True, they had become as dessicated as mummies, but they still needed air.

The first few coaches were passenger cars in which the S.S. travelled, the leaders and 200 soldiers of the death's head brigade. Their arms glinted threateningly in the sunshine. The prisoners knew that the end had come, but their apathy and their resignation were such that the will to live was almost completely extinct.

This journey towards death had reached its eighth day. They travelled across unknown territory and it seemed to them that the names of the stations figured only on the map of the devil. Even hunger hurt no more, though for the last three days they hadn't even received their bread-ration.

Suddenly the train slowed down and stopped.

The Rabbi of Prachnik lay on the floor of the cattle-truck, only half concious, but it seemed to him as if someone were calling his name.

"Rabbi Shapira! Rabbi Shapira! Is there a Jew by that name among you? Let him come immediately to the commander in the first coach."

What could the commander want with him? Nothing good, that was certain.

In the commanders compartment he was received by a squat nazi with a scarred face. He did not kick the rabbi nor did he hit him but he offered him a seat.

"Rabbi Shapira, I want to talk to you. You are the leader of the Jews, aren't you? A wise man, a clever man."

And he offered the rabbi a cigarette.

"I am going to reveal to you a great secret. I want to save your lives. I am sure you know what this train with its two hundred nazi soldiers means to you, don't you? Yes, I want to save you and I have only one request. When the Americans arrive, you must tell them that I have always treated you well. Haven't I behaved with great humanity?" he asked

the rabbi without, however, daring to look into his
eyes, for he knew that Belzebub had been but a
beginner compared to him. And now he was asking
Rabbi Shapira to intercede for him with the Americans!

"Go back to the others and pray to your God that
the Americans get here before noon tomorrow. Because I can't play this game much longer. The prisoners will now receive better rations."

But the Americans did not arrive.

The next day Rabbi Shapira was again summoned.
The commander seemed angry.

"You have not prayed well, rabbi. True, the Americans occupied the place where I was supposed to
take you for execution, but according to latest orders,
I am to carry out the execution in that little grove"
— and he pointed with his finger to a distant point
"I can delay it by another day at most. So hurry
and pray well now!"

The rabbi was about to leave when an S.S. colonel
entered the compartment.

"What is this swine doing here?" he yelled, strik-
ing the rabbi in the face.

The commander turned white and could not find
words to answer.

But Rabbi Shapira, though tottering under the

terrible blow, understood what was at stake and replied :

"I have come to ask the commander to distribute also tomorrow's rations today so that the men, in their weakness, should not have to stand in line twice."

The commander who had collected his wits in the meantime, made a sign of assent : "Yes, this is what the Jew came to see me about."

The colonel shrugged his shoulder as if he were thinking 'what difference does it make now. "Fulfil their request" he said.

Is was Wednesday and the guns of the Americans sounded quite close, but the Stars and Stripes still didn't show up.

"You see, your Creator refuses to save you," — shouted the commander having summoned the rabbi again and he abused God in an indescribable way.

"Wait until Friday morning, Commander," the Rabbi of Prachnik begged.

"All right, but I make you responsible. Friday morning at seven o'clock the Jews will line up and march, in the greatest silence, toward the little grove. I have to obey orders but I promise you that those who remain unhurt after the volley can run.

I won't have them pursued. The highway is quite near. If you reach it, you may still be saved.

Trembling in every limb, Rabbi Shapira turned to the nazi.

"Thank you for your good will, Commander, but let me beg you, don't hurry with the preparations tomorrow morning at seven. After all, orders can be carried out slowly. The Eternal Father may still help."

The S.S. looked at him in amazement.

"You still have hope, rabbi? What stubborn, extraordinary people you are, you Jews to keep on hoping to the last minute."

"It is not only to ask His help that we believe in the Creator," the rabbi replied, "we need His help also in the Afterworld."

It was Thursday evening. The rabbi returned to the cattle-truck and looked at his companions. They lay lifeless, most of them lacked the strength to rise. After long deliberation, he picked three young men who still looked strong enough and told them about the devilish plan for the morrow. He asked them to escape.

With great difficulty, after hours of hard work they succeeded in sawing through the iron bars of the little windowy. The three young men climbed out and from the three light thumps, Rabbi Shapira knew that they had reached ground. In the course of the night, the three deserters came out on to the highway and waited, hidden behind bushes, for dawn to come. They were just deliberating where to turn when the arrival of a tank put a stop to their conversation.

"Americans!" one of them exclaimed, and all three began running toward the tank waving white rags.

"Perhaps they won't even stop," the young men thought anxiously.

But suddenly the tank stopped. Its driver, an American Jew, noticed the three scarecrows in their striped clothes.

"Come, come quickly," the young men begged, "every second is valuable. They are this very minute lining up 2800 Jews for execution!

The two other Americans did not understand their words, but the Jew turned the tank in the indicated direction in spite of the loud protests of the other two who knew that this was against orders. The Jew had seen the handiwork of the nazis in the liberated areas and was aware what was at stake.

They arrived in the nick of time. The prisoners had lined up in the little grove in rows four deep.

They were waiting for the order to begin the massacre.

At the sight of the American tank, the nazis threw
away their guns and raised their arms to the sky.
They thought that more tanks were coming behind
the first. The Jews picked up the nazi guns and put
them out of reach. The commander tried to make
a run for it but a well aimed shot from the tank
brought him down.

"And do you know who that Jewish tank-driver
was?" Rabbi Shapira asked his breathless audience.
Then, without waiting for an answer, he pointed a
finger at the man from Pittsburg.

Pinchas Kohn was deeply embarrassed as he stood
amid the cross-fire of friendly glances.

Yet he had nothing to be ashamed of. His deed
will precede him in this world and beyond it, to the
end of time.

RECOVERED CHILDREN

RABBI Lipe Friedman, the Rebe of Udvard as he is called, lives in a little moshav lying between Tel-Aviv and Jerusalem. He had arrived in Eretz Israel eight years before with Hungarian immigrants from Roumania. The truth is that he could have settled in Jerusalem or any of the large towns had he so wanted, but he preferred life in a rural community.

In his home-town, Reb Lipe had not only filled the role of the "rav hatzoir", the young rabbi, but he had indeed, in the precise sense of the word, been the rabbi of youth. All who lived near him fell willy-nilly under his influence and imitated him in all his actions, be it work of charity or study. Yet he did not talk much, all he did was to show an example.

He had studied to be a rabbi under the guidance of his own father. The old man had had a very wide correspondence; everyone turned to him for advice, and for his halachic decisions. The father had always discussed whatever problems arose with his son and thus the young Reb Lipe acquired a knowledge so broad that not many of his age could vie with him. He was on the threshold of a brilliant carreer when. .

Yes, when the terrible blaze destroying the world put a stop to his expectations. The old rabbi went with his entire kehila to the place from where there is no return. Reb Lipe himself escaped in a way only akin to a miracle; but his family was lost. In the labour camp when, after the hard work to which he had never been used, he lay on his bunk, he dreamed about Eretz Yisroel. Yes, he would go there if he survived these horrors. He spoke to his companions of his plans, and when one of them asked:

"Don't you think there are enough rabbis in Eretz Yisroel?" he replied:

"Do you think I want to be a rabbi there? I shall be happy if I am lucky enough to work as an orange picker. . ."

After the war, at the first opportunity, he realized his dream and, on his arrival, organized a group and settled in a moshava. Soon the moshava began to prosper. The families lived happily and in peace, from the income gained by the cultivation of the land and by animal farming. It was a real Jewish life, a healthy, strengthening existence.

At harvest time the rabbi went out into the fields

to give expert advice on the tithes, the "trumo" and the "maaser". He was always there when good advice or speedy help were required; but he himself remained modestly in the background and expected no appreciation. On Sabbaths for the Third Meal, the members of the group always met at his house to enjoy his glowing words of Torah.

Those are happy moments when the last rays of the setting sun takes leave of the Sabbath! With a pious heart, Rabbi Lipe begins intoning "bne hecholo," and the subsequent songs are sung by others in turn. One could only hope that time would stop and preserve those moments for ever! It is impossible to describe the Sabbath afternoon mood of a moshav in Eretz Yisroel, where, during the day, the soul has dipped into the beauties of the Torah, where people live according to the commands of the Torah and where everyone seemed swayed by some exceptional, almost transcendent feeling.

At such times, Reb Lipe took advantage of the solemn mood of his hearers and, almost ecstatically, spoke of the tasks of Jewry, of the preciousness of the Torah.

From time to time he travelled into the town, usually to Jerusalem, but occasionally he would visit Bne-Brak, to spend some hours in the Yeshivas. He

conversed with the teachers but it was with the
bocherim that he maintained real friendship. These
young men interested him deeply; he answered their
questions, solved their problems, enquired about their
private lives and, when it was necessary, offered
financial aid. More than once he was invited to
become a rabbi, but he always refused and buried
himself in his self-appointed "exile".

But there was something else that also attracted
him to the towns. Many outstanding, famous zadik-
im were arriving for visits from abroad and Reb
Lipe never missed an opportunity to spend a Sabbath in their company. This was also an opportunity
to meet old friends and acquaintances, to have long
and intimate conversations about past events and to
discuss marriages. His daughter was approaching the
age of wedlock. One of the secret purposes of these
travels was to find a suitable husband for her. Yet,
there was something even more important concealed
behind that lively interest.

Reb Lipe had never been able to resign himself to
the maddening thought that his children had
perished. He could not believe that they were no
longer alive. Somehow, he had the feeling that one
of his sons was still living and, as time went on, he
became more and more convinced that this son was

waiting for him somewhere. He even thought of returning to Poland to search for him there. The little boy who occupied his thoughts, had been a fair child with blue eyes, and he had heard that some of the Jewish children had been placed with nazi families to make up for the "loss of blood" and grow into good Germans. He was constantly tormented by such thoughts and the compulsion to go and find that child of his gave him no rest. That was why he sought the company of young men, that was why he asked them to tell him the story of their lives, hoping that somehow he would be led to trace his child.

One day, Reb Lipe received the news that a certain rabbi from America was coming to Eretz Yisroel. He was coming for a few weeks accompanied by other rabbis and their pupils. Reb Lipe had once been friendly with the Rabbi of K., they still wrote to each other and recalled the days they spent together in a German labour camp. After the war, the Rabbi of K. had gone to America where he soon attracted a wide circle of followers. He gained fame and recognition among thousands of Jews there. Now he had decided to visit the Holy Land.

The news made Reb Lipe very happy and he travelled to Lydda to welcome the Zadik at the airfield. A large and enthusiastic crowd had assembled to greet the famous guest. When the Rabbi of K. alighted from the plane, he immediately recognized his old friend and embraced and kissed him. They could not talk at leisure right there and it was only on the following evening, when Reb Lipe visited his friend at his quarters that they could converse undisturbed.

After the first warm greetings, the Rabbi of K. asked Reb Lipe whether he was happy in Eretz Yisroel and how he lived.

"Boruch Hashem" Reb Lipe replied, "I have everything I want but something is tormenting me and there is a terrible weight on my soul. I cannot forget my children, but I don't have to tell you this."

A deep sigh rose from the Zadik's breast. He could indeed understand his friend's emotions for he too had been struck the same blow, and lost his wife and children. After the war, however, he had remarried.

Reb Lipe experienced a strange feeling while he was with his friend, the Zadik, as if some wonderful melody were ringing in his soul. Only on sacred feasts is one seized with similar feelings, after a prayer recited with burning fervour.

The conversation lasted until late into the night.

Sitting on the open terrace under the stars, they recalled on this warm June night many a common memory and relived the past in their hearts.

"When we last met," Reb Lipe said, "we were celebrating the seder at the labour camp. We sang holy melodies and, in soothing festive atmosphere, the suffering expressions and mute participation of our brethren seemed like the foliage of a mysterious forest nodding in agreement. We were seated at the seder table that night, bathing in the phosphorescent light emanating from you, Rabbi. I shall never forget the tear-stained eyes, the weeping faces of the men, torn from their families. Later two peasants came to speak to you. . ."

"Yes, I remember," the rabbi said raising his large dark eyes to Reb Lipe, "an old chasid was waiting for me outside, one who knew me well because he had studied with my grandfather. He had come to warn me that the entire camp would be transported to Germany the next day. He told me to flee. A mutual friend, Jankl Davidovits, had paid a large sum of money in the hope of saving me at any cost. I struggled with myself all through that night. I thought and meditated but I could not make up my mind whether I had the right to save myself while my brethren were going to certain death. And yet, could I help them by perishing with them? And yet could I leave them? At such fateful moments one has to show an example of courage. Finally the Creator showed me the solution: pleto, pletosenu — we must escape. I don't know whether you understood me because the two gendarmes brought by the peasants and the chasid yelled at me that if I spoke they would shoot me dead. The money, the ransom, was already in their pockets. I hope you understood and appreciated my position. . ."

"Of course, I understood," Reb Lipe replied, "we were constantly planning to escape ever since some of the labour units had been "entrained" to Germany. I went in quickly and called to our friends to escape! Yes, but where? Nobody could answer that question. Some immediately disappeared, while others could not make up their minds which direction to take how to get away without money, surrounded by enemies. I did not meditate long, because I had hidden one of my sons with a peasant family in a village and for him I had to remain alive. I walked fast for about an hour, then hid in a depression in the forest. Soon I heard the voices of the pursuers but, thanks be to the Creator, it began to rain and the water washed away my footprints."

Now it was again the rabbi who picked up the

thread of memories. He was obviously very agitated because his forehead was covered with beads of perspiration.

"The gendarmes bribed by my friends took me by car toward the Roumanian frontier under cover of the night. I begged them to drive through a certain village where I had hidden my child with peasants. At the time of our deportation, the child had contracted typhoid and was taken in by the peasants from the shelter of the priest. But I begged in vain, the gendarmes feared for their own lives. In my despair, I began to shout and threaten that I would jump from the car. Then I offered them my gold watch. The last argument proved effective. One of them promised to return for the child and meet me at the frontier at nine o'clock in the morning. He stood by his word. He acquired another car and drove back to the village. No sooner had we reached the frontier than he appeared with the child. The gendarmes took my watch and handed me the child. It was wrapped in a blanket and I did not see its face. We climbed back into the car and never stopped until the frontier was far behind us. There I unwrapped the child, and to my greatest surprise, it was not mine. Mine was a girl and the one in my lap a little boy."

"Rabbi, Rabbi!" Reb Lipe cried out, beside himself with excitement, "go on, tell me what was the name of the village where your child was hidden? Rabbi, my life depends on your answer."

The rabbi looked at his friend amazed. He could not understand the sudden excitement and tried to calm him down.

"Is that so very important? The name of the village was N."

Reb Lipe shook from head to foot.

"Rabbi, it is my child you saved, my little boy who was hidden with a peasant of the village you mentioned. The peasant's name was Vasij. When I came out of the forest the next morning I went directly to his house. The peasant told me that my boy had been taken away by gendarmes in the middle of the night. He said that it was lucky the gendarmes did not find the other child, a little girl, who was sleeping in his wife's bed."

"Reb Lipe," the rabbi cried, "that little girl was my daughter, the gendarmes made a mistake!"

"I took that little girl with me," Reb Lipe continued quietly, "I carried her across the Roumanian frontier on my back. The peasant was glad to get rid of his dangerous ward."

"The rabbi could hardly contain himself.

"Speak, Reb Lipe, speak, what happened to that little girl, is she still alive?"

"I brought her with me to Eretz Yisroel and treated her as my own daughter. She is my little Lea. And what happened to my son, my little Smulke?"

"I took him with me to America and brought him up as my son. He is young Shmuel who is here with me."

The first sheaves of red beams now appeared on the eastern horizon, messengers of a beautiful summer day. The rabbi and Reb Lipe went into the house. Everyone was asleep, only the hearts of the two men sang with a surfeit of happiness.

THEY WERE TWELVE HUNDRED

To the memory of the martyrs of Auschwitz

FEW New Year's Days, few Rosh Hashonos such as this one have been recorded in history.

The Jew who found a Shofar — nobody knew where — and held it in his hand, ran almost frenziedly from one group to the other between the barracks. He blew the Shofar as prescribed in the rules, with the tekios, schevorim, trios. Never has such a tearful sound reached the ears of man. The sound of the Shofar rose towards the skies weeping, begging for forgiveness, demanding salvation.

And the man, who had, by some miracle, obtained a Shofar, blew it some fifty times, sending its mournful message to the four winds to help his brethren on this memorable New Year's Day to fulfil, on Rosh Hashono, the Command to blow the Shofar.

Only a few days before, the S.S. executioners had invented a new game to amuse themselves. The knowledge that they could dip their hands at pleasure into the blood of the herds of sheep brought to this slaughterhouse, was constant fuel to their vile, perverted, inhuman imagination. They surpassed one another in devising new and more original diversions.

One of these Prussian brutes, for instance, conceived the idea of piling up heaps of cabbage and potato peelings approximately a hundred yards one from the other.

"Los!" he yelled, "Run Jews, there's your slop."

Forgetting the devilish purpose behind these daily brain-waves, the unfortunate, starving herd ran head over heels toward the life-giving garbage.

"Stop, my brethren, stop. Can't you see that you are running toward destruction!"

But it is too late. The faces of the executioners break into satanic grins, bullets burst from the machinegun. Those who ran so desperately to prolong their lives lie dead in a bloody heap. The master marksmen had found their target.

The witness who has survived the torments of this hell, describes innumerable such bestial murders committed for the mere pleasure of killing in those days of horror.

The massacre of the children, planned for the day of Rosh Hashono, was also the fruit of the playful ideas conceived in the diseased minds of those sickly sentimental and inhumanly cruel adherents of Wotan. The S.S. had decided that there were too many Jewish children between the ages of twelve and fifteen still alive.

"It is time to thin out the brood," the commander of the murderers had decreed.

And on a hot, sunny afternoon the army of trembling children, clad in rough striped prison uniforms, was ordered to march past two stakes stuck into the ground. One was shorter, the other taller, approximately 130-140 centimetres high. The child whose head reached the top of the taller stake was safe. The smaller children were destined for the gas-chamber.

Devilish playfulness! Horrible games! One thousand two hundred beloved Jewish child-martyrs. Your little heads did not reach the top of the stake, not even when you stood on tiptoe. My tears flow eternally at the memory of your tragic fate. May the Creator revenge your death and that of the other six million martyrs!

We know, yes, we know, that most of us do not achieve the perfection of humanity; how then can we expect dignified, human behaviour from the unfortunate victims of those dreadful days that deprived even the strongest of their sober judgment. The frames of life fell asunder and so did the souls. Life was the cheapest commodity of all. Is it then surprising that few could resist the desire to live, only to live, even at the price of the blood of others!

Judge not, brother. Who knows what you would have done in my place, what you would have done when you saw your child whom you had saved in the face of a thousand perils, march toward the gaschamber. There, hidden among your ragged clothes, are the torn banknotes, the gold, the dollars for which you once toiled until you dropped with fatigue. All the treasures of the world you would give to save your child!

I ask you, could you have resisted the temptation, the sin? For the Torah considers it sin to save a soul at the price of another.

Because this is what happened. For each child claimed back from death in exchange for a small fortune, another was substituted. For each child returned to its parents, the devils took one of the "saved" to make up the number.

And there were those who considered this permissible!

A man from Vac, a pious, godfearing man approached his rabbi and whispered:

"Rabbi, here is money, hidden under my shirt. May I offer it to the S.S. guard to save my only child whom I have so often brought back from the brink of death?"

The father and the rabbi wept bitterly together but the rabbi made no reply.

The father took the rabbi's silence as a negative answer; if the rabbi says nothing, then this is the Command of the Torah. And the tormented little Jew from Vac drew himself up proudly like Hannah, the martyr of Maccabean times who sent seven of her children bravely to death, and said:

"Rabbi, I am happy that my son will die according to the Command of the Torah."

But this was not the only Din Torah of the rabbi who incidentally, was the man who had blown the Shofar.

A little boy of about thirteen came to speak to him, a well developed, tall boy, who had attained the required size and thus been saved. In tears he told the rabbi that his best friend, a boy older than he but shorter, was now among the condemned. That boy had been his teacher, his "bocher" in the Yeshiva, his name was Mordche, he was a Talmid Chochem, and his death would be a terrible loss.

"Mordche could grow into a great man." he re-peated stubbornly. "He is a much better scholar than I and I would gladly give my life for him."

The rabbi asked the little boy to desist.

"Our laws do not allow that one should give up his life for another."

"Tell me at least, rabbi that this would not be considered suicide Up there."

The rabbi could no longer contain himself, he broke into bitter sobs.

"No, my sweet child, I cannot tell you that."

The day of Rosh Hashana arrived. Nature wrap-ped itself into a grey mist, the colour of lead. Up there in heaven the fate of the world and of the beloved people, Israel, was again being decided. What shall become of us, our Father, our King, if you have no mercy on us? Shall not one of the custodians of Your Name survive? And yet Your children obey Your command even in the darkest depths of hell."

Ever since dawn, the rabbi had kept walking from one group to another. Loudly he recited the benediction and the people resorted to their last stores of moral strength and answered "Amen". They closed their eyes tightly to concentrate on the course of the Shofar's sound with the whole of their thoughts. Even their breathing was but a desperate prayer.

The children in the special barrack, the death-house, heard the sound of the Shofar. They sent word that they too wanted to fulfil the command of the Creator for the last time. Let the rabbi come to them with the Shofar.

Those outside, the adults, were divided in their opinions about this. Entering the death-house involved terrible danger. The transportation of the condemned to the crematorium was planned for the evening hours. A bell would ring when the barrack doors closed for the last time. It was growing late. To go in there required real fortitude. But the rabbi who blew the Shofar did not hesitate. He stole into the death-house.

The one thousand and two hundred children sat on the floor of the barrack in a closely knit circle. Their faces burned with the fire of self-sacrifice as if the souls of the ten Tanaitic martyrs had come to life in them, as they prepared.to hand themselves to their executioners. Their hearts beat high, overflowing with the emotions that had filled the hearts of martyrs in all times. They were ready to give their lives for their Creator, for Kidush Hashem, for the Sanctification of the Holy Name.

The rabbi's face turned ashen when he laid his eyes on the sacred assembly prepared for death. Words stuck in his throat, his heart almost stopped beating and his soul swelled with sentiments that one experiences but once in a lifetime.

"Rabbi, speak to us before blowing the Shofar," the boys begged.

And the rabbi obeyed. He spoke words that had never left his lips either before or since. He spoke of the greatness of the martyrs and recalled their names and deeds through the ages. Then he concluded:

"And yet, my children, trust the Father Eternal, because man must hope for delivery even with the knife at his throat."

There are no words to describe the solemnity of that moment, the burning eyes of the children. their transfigured expression as they took upon themselves the Creator's yoke, the duty of martyrdom, for the Glory of His Sacred Name.

And they began to sing the Psalm: Lamnatzeach. Never since the birth of Judaism has this song soared to such heights, never has it expressed the Jewish fate, the tragedy of this most persecuted, yet greatest people of the earth with such unbearable beauty.

But none of the children felt that their fate was tragic.

Is it a tragedy to ascend the loftiest peak of heroism and perfection at an innocent age, to become purified of the filth of all ages for the Jewish ideal?

After the blowing of the Shofar, the Jewish children surrounded the rabbi. There stood Mordche, the Talmid Chochem, who had apparently been elected leader by the children. Mordche raised his voice in the deep silence:

"We children, who are going to our deaths and giving our lives for our Creator, thank the rabbi for having come to us and made it possible for us to perform this last commandment. We beg the Eternal Father to permit him and his children to survive these horrors."

"Amen" one thousand and two hundred voices replied.

The time had come for the rabbi to leave. No sooner had he gone through the door of the barrack than the alarm bell began to ring. All entrances to the death-house were locked.

Later, all could hear the patter of the children's feet, the glorious tread of the one thousand and two hundred martyrs on the road to immortality.

THE CHASIDIM

THE air in the dark Beth Hamidrash is heavy and oppressive. Night has fallen on the town and only infrequently do distant noises disturb the silence, only rarely does a light from outside illuminate the faces of those sitting within.

The American tourist in the expensive light grey suit had stopped me in the street asking me to show him "the real old Jerusalem." I had taken him into a Beth Hamidrash, where "Shalashudes", the Sabbath afternoon meal was in progress.

The melodies rising from the depth of the soul and the subsequent silences are a preliminary to the intensification of fervour. A hundred or a hundred and twenty souls soar with enraptured yearning toward the heavens. The sacred mood of the Sabbath welds them together, they have thrown off the burdens of the weekdays, the cares of their toil, that they may rise.

Outside, in the town, everything pulsates with the joy of life, the buses are already running, pour-

ing forth crowds of people who are seeking the
pleasures of the week-end at various places of
amusement.

In the Beth Hamidrash the quiet murmur is like
the whispering of ancient oaks in a primeval forest.

What can this spectacle reveal to a stranger
brought here by chance? Does it, even for a moment
reveal true life to the materialist? The newcomer
from the outside is suddenly saddened as if he had
found a lonely island, an impassable road in the
midst of a forest. "Are there still true souls, believers in this world?" he askes himself in his astonish
ment.

Earthiness, which was in such full blast outside,
crept into the place, but the men within fight like
lions to preserve their souls on the level of ecstasy.
They fight with all their strength against the influence of mundane thoughts.

The outside world has little knowledge of how
they struggle to be worthy to serve the Creator. A
flame burns in the heart of each one of them but
they are besieged by the resistance of the world
without. At times it reduces their strength, but in
here, in the Beth Hamidrash, the sacred yearning
blazes high. Outside, passions whirl, the vibrations
of the radio, the cinema, the theatre permeate dazed

senses with a sickly-sweet poison and contaminate souls with a tormenting, inextinguishable thirst for pleasure.

In the Beth Hamidrash, the atmosphere is imbued with a sacred yearning and force of faith links those present into a single chain of steel.

It is a superhuman task to fight against the false passions of the world. This knowledge embitters even their happiest moments and saddens their souls.

The singing increases in volume, the deep baritone of the adults blends with the sweet soprano of the children and somewhere a beautiful tenor takes up the lead.

How is it possible that such singing should rise with such miraculous harmony without some form of organization, without a conductor? The composer of the song, the great Zadik, grips the souls of his followers, his pupils, from the distant Afterworld, his teachings are incorporated in these singing men and their lips form his hymn.

"This is the essence of the song" — I tell the enquiring visitor — "only those who accept the teachings of the great Zadik, can come close to the secret."

"How can a prayer to the Creator rise from the

hearts of the exhausted children of the age that survived the German hell and whose relatives were burned in the crematoria of Auschwitz? We have been witnesses of the moral decay of Jewry after the war, of the rapid spread of immorality. How can a worker weighed down with everyday worries, undertake the service of the Eternal Father which demands such sacrifice, such renunciation?"

Instead of replying, I invite the visitor to approach the table where the Rabbi has just begun to speak.

The songs come to an end, one hears the patter of feet in the darkness. Those thirsty for knowledge crowd forward so as not to miss a single word. Suddenly the entire room is steeped in deep silence.

Then, in the silence, the rabbi, heir to the throne of the great Zadik, begins to speak. His voice is muffled by tears but the text is quiet and gentle:

"In our days," he says clearly, "in this last period before the arrival of the Messiah, the chasid, the militant servant of the Creator, can no longer be as he was at the time of the Baal Shem and his disciples. The task we have to accomplish today is different and therefore our instruments must also be different. To help souls to rise to the Creator,

is the command of the Torah that must be unconditionally obeyed; we need men who are ready at
any moment to sacrifice every advantage for the
fulfilment of the Creator's command.

Unfortunately, the chasid of today has to stand
many a test. Therefore, the longing hidden in the
depths of his heart must be strengthened by all
manner of outside expression and must be empha-
sised by externals. If we do not eat greedily today,
if we have the strength to lay down the spoon when
we are still hungry, we serve the Creator and the
search for truth as our predecessors did before with
their fasting. By dressing modestly, we keep ourselves aloof from harmful company and thereby
fortify our camp and achieve better results than if
we organised debates on how to fight against dis-
loyalty.

And let our faithfulness to truth be our main
principle. By honouring our pledged word we com-
pel our opponents to respect us."

The rabbi spoke in a tone of such overwhelming
conviction and sincerily, that the visitor was deeply
moved.

"It is really wonderful" was his comment to me.

The light went up. Simple working men were
standing in a circle, their faces transfigured, shin-

ing with a pure light, their eyes filled with a higher faith.

"It is indeed wonderful," I answered, and I wished that I could perpetuate this impression, this feeling in his soul. "Imagine the distance dividing the profane world from our little sland here. We have found the truth and live consistently for it. The Eternal Father created the world, created men, and he created them for his service. With our limited capacities and limited strength we are trying to make the service perfect. We must exile selfishness from our lives and we must understand our insignificance compared to the greatness of the Creator. Our aim is not the satis faction of passions, nor money, nor power, but to hallow the name of the Creator, to experience and to spread the truth. The whole world is against us with its selfishness and sins. The saddest thing of all is that not only the ignorant and inferior masses but even men of science and intellect have taken the wrong road. Even the scientist errs if he does not subordinate human purpose to the Creator."

"What you are saying," the visitor replied with a smile "is that the entire world should follow the road pointed out by the Beth Hamidrash?"

"Yes. Our hopes show the positive road. The

world awaits its destruction but we await the arrival of the true Saviour, the Messiah."

And thus we took leave of each other.

E. Snitkovsky

ESCAPE AT CHANUKA

RABBI Gamliel was greatly beloved in his place of birth, the town of Sz. in Hungary. He had brought up hundreds of pupils with great selflessness. He prepared the children for the yeshiva, he was the "melamed" of the twelve to thirteen year old boys. He watched strictly over their observance of the commandments, never deviating by an iota from the law. He himself steered clear of the ways of the Chasidim but he did not protect his pupils with the same fierceness from the ways of the Baal Shem. Whenever he heard that one or other dressed in a chasidic way, he smiled with satisfaction and tried to minimize the "sin" of the wayward child even to the parents.

As far as he was concerned, he remained to the end a loyal preserver of the traditions of the Chasam Sofer even during the tragedy of the Hungarian Jews, during the Rakosi era. After the grim days of servitude, came the revolution. Rabbi Gamliel heard more and more frequently news about the fortunate people who had succeeded in crossing the frontier and he too began to weave plans of escape

The party of escaping people he joined were not too pleased with the presence among them of this old, white- bearded Jew. They murmured to each other, shrugging their shoulders, that such an ancient was a burden upon his companions, until, at last, one of them took the old man under his wing :

"How could we leave this pious old man to fend for himself? We might need the merit of a good deed. Perhaps it will save us at the hour of decision."

The escapees planned the crossing of the frontier for the hours of the night. The guide assured them that there would be no difficulty. The frontier guards would look in the other direction, he repeated. They left on the outskirts of the town. From there they had to walk only 10-12 kilometres to the border. where they hid in a deserted army camp. The camp was surrounded by a barbed wire fence but the guide knew exactly where to get across and they all came through unscathed. However, the frontier guards were still vigilant and drove them back with fixed bayonets. The group became desperate and nervous, only Rabbi Gamliel remained calm. He even made jokes, his wit sparkled and soon he had them all laughing.

"You know" the old man said "the Yoim Kippur avoide comes to an end only after three 'veanachnu korim'. This reference to their attempts to advance on all fours, made the members of the company laugh but Rabbi Gamliel said very seriously:

"You laugh and you don't care how distressed and tormented I am."

"What torments you, uncle Gamliel?"

"Today is the first evening of Chanuka. Where shall I light the Chanuka candles?"

It was getting on towards midnight. The smugglers succeeded in bribing one of the frontier guards to lead them out of the camp, and they set out in the frosty night towards the frontier. At last, they reached no-man's land. They found a wooden shed and decided to spend the remaining part of the night within it. Nobody was happier than Rabbi Gamliel. He quickly took from his rucksack the silver menorah and the Chanuka candles and made his preparations to light the first flame with the shehechyonu blessing.

"What are doing, Rabbi Gamliel?" his companions asked him in amazement. "You will attract the attention of the Russian patrol and then all will be lost."

But Rabbi Gamliel bade them keep calm.

"Nothing can happen to him who observes the commandment," he said quietly and began the ceremony.

Nobody protested any longer because they had all fallen under his spell. Perhaps also because they had become aware of the old man's exaltation. The whole group gathered around the rabbi.

No sooner had the first benediction been recited to the end, when the door of the hut was flung open from outside. A Russian officer stood in the door with his gun pointed at them; but, in the next second, the officer's arm dropped and his feet seemed nailed to the ground. He couldn't take a single step forward. He stared at the rabbi standing before the menora in solemn ecstasy with wide open eyes as if he were experiencing a vision.

"Ik ok Jid." he stammered in broken Yiddish, "tate majne chabadnik lubavitch."

Then he motioned to Rabbi Gamliel to go on with the prayer. The old man recited the prayer at first in a hesitating voice which, however, grew stronger and more ringing. He recited the shehechyonu that seemed today more significant than ever before in his life. Then he sang, and his companions accompanied the melody humming softly.

Suddenly the door opened again. Another group of refugees was seeking shelter in the hut. They had lost their way and were wandering about aimlessly in the freezing cold November night until they were led to to the hut by the light showing through the cracks. They noticed the Russian soldier only after they had entered. They recoiled, scared, but the Russian smiled at them reassuringly. "One of us" he said. The song that arose into the air was a veritable hymn of thankful hearts. "Nisim bayomim hahem, bizman haze." Finally, in honour of the guest, Rabbi Gamliel intoned the melody known as "Tanya" to the Chabad Chasidim. This song shook the Russian to the very core of his being. Looking at the rabbi standing before him with his patriarchal appearance, his face transfigured, he remembered his parents' home, his childhood, the chanuka evenings as celebrated in his youth. His eyes filled with tears. "The Jewish spark had burst into flame." Rabbi Gamliel thought.

Dawn was breaking. In the meantime, the newcomers had brought out thermos flasks and the refugees refreshed themselves with hot tea. The Russian officer took a hip-flask filled with vodka from his pocket and offered it around. It was a fiery, warming drink that instilled new life into the tired limbs.

The Russian officer opened the door and peered out.

"The next patrol will be along soon. Get ready and leave because they won't go easy on you if they catch you."

"Who knows, perhaps one day, we shall meet in Jerusalem. That is where the road to freedom leads."

GRANDFATHER FROM BLUZHOV

I was then a young married man. My chin was just beginning to sprout a beard. The happiness of the first year of my marriage and the increasing responsibility of my task seemed to have drawn a rosy curtain over my life. Few can have been granted that absolute feeling of serenity I then enjoyed. At least, that is how I see it today from the distance of many years.

In fact, it was from no ordinary assortment that my soul had been handed down me. I was the grandson of the Rabbi of Bluzhov and related to the Zadik of Dinov. Both my father and mother could trace their family trees back to King David. This noble dynasty had been known through the ages for its exemplary discipline and its profound thinking. It constituted an extraordinary aristocracy linked by stronger ties to heaven that to the ball of mud we call earth. If I recall the ethereal world of my youth I can only regard it as a heavenly gift, that I had received without effort, ready made, by the merit of my ancestors. Nor was this all: by the Creator's favour I had been reared almost like a royal child and thus the diamond hidden in the depths of my soul did not remain concealed in its prison but was uncovered and brought to the light.

Who formed, who polished the gem of my soul?

Who if not the awe-inspiring prince: Grand father!

You did not know Grandfather, you were too young to have met him, but the truth is that had you been worthy of appearing before this Titan with his eyebrows meeting, hiding behind the dense smoke curling up from his long pipe, what would you have seen? How much would you have guessed of his extraordinary strength and greatness?

For your soul is no diamond, at best it is gold or silver, nickel or copper, perhaps only iron, or not even that, only mud. I do not intend to hurt you, you are what you have become. Your souls have been roughened in the fire of unrestrained passions by your fathers and mothers, your grand-fathers and God knows how many ancestors. The treasure of your soul has been turned into peat in the course of long centuries.

My soul was protected by my parents but, especi-ally, by my grandfather. He gave me much of his time. I was his favourite, together with my little sister. He loved us both dearly. Why? Because we obeyed his wishes.

The army of Chasidim, — there were more than a thousand of them — young and old, rich and poor, noble and wise, and even the family sincerely hated the chief Gabbai, Gimpl.

My sister and I were on good terms with him and this won us the love of our Grandfather. For Gimpl was the touchstone; only persons who liked Gimpl were permitted to appear before his face, everyone else immediately lost his favour. In general, Gimpl was considered a very disagreeable man. The five attendants belonging to Grandfather's retinue trembled before him. For Gimple ruled over everyone like a chancellor. The keys to the cashbox were always in his pocket and whatever was needed in the house had to be asked of him. When the Kvitlach were handed in, honourable old men, great scholars, lay-heads of communities, humiliated themselves before him. And how mercilessly Gimpl pursued the "Sheine Yidden" when, with a tumult, they arrived and demanded to see my Grandfather! Gimpl turned them out as if they were undesirable elements. In vain did they plead that they belonged to the family. They could rant and shout, but

Gimpl chased them away. He could not be circumvented, and anyone of whom he disapproved, could not see Grandfather.

This is how the distribution of the "remainders" took place. A whole boiled chicken was brought in to Grandfather .It had to be a whole chicken because he desired it that way although he hardly ate any of it and gave away the rest. Who ruled over the left-over meat? Gimpl. As this despot had an excellent appetite, he devoured almost all of it; only a neck or a wing and a few little bones were left. Eyes pleaded with him from every side: "Leave us something, just a little scrap!" For even a crumb from the Rabbi's table was equivalent to a blessing. Gimpl did not dress like a chasid; he trimmed his beard and wore a short jacket like the Germans. He stood out among Grandfather's environment. It was rumoured that Grandfather could have had ten times as many followers had he not been so strongly attached to this strange, repulsive and haughty person.

Yet whenever this question was raised, Grandfather, the Rabbi of Bluzhov, answered with a mysterious smile. It almost seemed as if he had no need for the whole lot of them with their copper, iron and mud souls.

Gimpl continued to enjoy his favour. What is more, the awe-inspiring Grandfather with his joined eye-brows, stood before the despotic bachelor like a humble servant before his all-powerful master. If Gimpl objected to something — and he usually did so in a very rude way — Grandfather withdrew like a humiliated schoolboy.

I remember that I once asked Grandfather for a larger sum of money for the family of a talmid-chochem. He made a sign to me to indicate that Gimpl would soon leave the room and we could then discuss it. It was evening, time for the distribution to the poor of the money brought in with the Kvitlach. A large pile of money was on the table. I stood behind my Grandfather's chair. Many people came, they told him of their needs and waited. Grandfather's brows rose high over the half-closed lids. Dense smoke came out of his pipe as from a crater. Then, for a moment, Gimpl left the room. Grandfather quickly scooped up a pile of banknotes and pushed them into his cigar-pocket. He had taken it for me, for my poor friends. But Gimpl was already back. He sniffed suspiciously and looked at the table. The room was full of people and all watched Gimpl, waiting with bated breath. Gimpl's face turned a fiery red, even his neck blushed, then he began to screech like a madman. His repulsive voice cut like a whip.

"What has that snotty young man been doing again?" — then he turned to Grandfather and yelled at him :

"What is this, are we stealing again? Stealing again? Put back that money where it belongs."

Grandfather turned pale and then, like a shame-faced little boy caught in a prank, pulled the bank-notes from his cigar-pocket and put them back on the table. Gimpl picked up the money and stuck it quickly into his own pocket.

After a while, the chasidim grew tired of this unrestrained despotism and accused Gimpl ever more loudly of mishandling the money. The accusation became generally known and the younger men wanted the older chasidim to form a delegation to my Grandfather and complain against Gimpl.

At first, the elder men did not want to stick out their necks. What? That they should simply break in on Grandfather? Do you know who Grandfather was? Even the ministering angels trembled under a glance from his eye! There was not a single movement, or half-movement, with which he did not join worlds, even a motion of his little finger sufficed for that! Should the older men, those who

revered him most deeply, rebel against him? They
who melted in the fires of his lofty soul, should they
disturb his mood?

But the accusations against Gimpl became so
loud and general that there was no way of avoiding
it. That step had to be taken; and, one day, the
old men stood before Grandfather, their knees
trembling, the words sticking in their throats.

"Gimpl. . ."

Grandfather raised his terrible brows and his
ears began to waggle, a sign of extreme anger.
Then he pronounced the annihilating verdict:

"He who judges the deeds of his Master is as
if he were critisising Shechina."

And with this the audience was ended.

The poor, humiliated, silly little old men sat in
the waiting room weeping until my Grandfather
felt sorry for them and sent word that they were
forgiven.

Gimpl's position remained solid as a rock. It was
obligatory not only to respect him but to love him
as well.

I had learned a great deal from Grandfather in
those unforgettable hours when we remained alone
in the room and he shared with me his solitude.
Particularly the hours of the night were intimate;

I felt as if he were opening wide windows for me through which I could watch the world pullulating in the depths, all the vanities and the frailties called human life. It was as if I were looking down upon a distant mole-hill from a castle built on a high cliff. The secret and revealed wisdoms gushed from this gigantic source, irresistibly as if he were the original source itself. His every word was a prophecy, a glimpse into the distant future.

Let me recall but one conversation. We were meditating about an involved halachic question, whether it should be considered suicide if someone, though not dying by his own hand, permitted by passive resignation that death conquer him.

I represented the point of view that according to the word of the Law, only the hastening of death, in one way or another, is to be considered suicide, and thus a sin.

I recall that when I uttered these words, Grandfather snatched at my arm with unwonted passion. A small candle was burning in the room, the light of the moon through the open window, and in this grotesque double light I saw Grandfather's awe-inspiring face and there were tears in his eyes.

"No, no!" he shouted at me so loud that I recoiled "know once and for all that he who does nothing to prevent death is also committing a sin, that too is suicide!"

Not much later Grandfather dismissed me. I was groping down the dark stairs when he threw open his door and recalled me.

"Don't forget, my son," he said very distinctly and the tears were still shining in his eyes "it is suicide if someone resigns himself to death, if he permits his fate to fulfil itself."

On the wooden planks that formed my bed in the camp, I call to my soul : Where are you? Where have you gone, descendant of princes, royal scion? The convolutions of my brain are injured by suffering, by years of torment. The beams cannot hold up much longer this tottering edifice! The silence of the grave lies over the camp and outside the S.S. blood-hounds are howling.

I am lying on wooden planks in the camp of Janow with the other deportees. While my soul shone like a diamond, my guardian angel was always with me on my fantastic travels, accompanying me through years of starvation, freezing, whippings. But now I have become lethargic. A terrible fashion was spreading among my fellow prisoners, the skeleton-men :— suicide. Before, when the radiation of my soul had gathered strength and warmth within me, I was the one who protested most loudly against this dreadful sin. But now I am lying on the planks, half-concious, in the throes of a horrible semi-sleep. Then suddenly as if I were coming to my senses, an unknown force begins to drum on my chest. In the afternoon I agreed with Lezer, who was working side by side with me, that today we would not go to fetch the soup, a horrible concoction of suspicious colour that never contained anything but a few beetroots; and yet, it gave life.

In the camp, if someone gets tired of living, he simply stops rising from his bunk, stops fighting for his breakfast, and the rest is easy. Lezer and I decided that we would not join the queue for food. Let the curtain fall.

I lay on my planks in a condition bordering on the transcendent. I knew that soon the last thread binding me to the areas this side of the border would break.

And then a strange change took place within me. As if a force beyond me had again lit the extinct flame of my soul, as if, in the complete darkness, a strong lamp had been lit, a blinding light, as from a reflector, struck my eyeballs and in the glaring brilliance, I saw a supernatural, phosphorescent apparition.

Grandfather!

There he stood, with his joined eyebrows and pale ivory face, as if we were arguing about a "Sugye" and I were saying:

"According to the word of the law, only if someone hastens death in one way or another, is it to be considered a sin."

I saw Grandfather's face twitch and passionately he snatched at my arm:

"No, no, my son," he shouted "know once and for all that he who does nothing to prevent death is also committing a sin, that too is suicide!"

The apparition disappeared. But the will to live revived in me. You came at the last moment, Grandfather, I thank you. You foresaw my fate. That is why you implanted the law so deeply in my soul. Your gaze, scanning the future, saw the terrible suffering of your grandson and his struggle with himself in the camp of Janow.

And I, who was half dead already, revived under the effect of this miraculous vision, I jumped from my bunk and ran to my friend and fellow-prisoner Lezer.

"Tomorrow, we shall stand in line with the others for soup! We shall fight for life, we shall live, because we have been sentenced to life!"

A MOTHER'S CHOICE

ALL Poland was drowning in blood and tears. Nazi jackboots trampled over everybody and everything. There were hardly any men left in Drohobyce. Almost all of them had been driven to the outskirts of the town to dig trenches; and when the long ditches were finished they found out that they had been digging their own graves. The S.S. soldiers made them stand in line along the ditches and after the machinegun fire had ceased they had shovelled earth on top of them. The earth heaved and writhed for a long while but it could not cast up the victims who were buried alive. After a time the earth stopped moving, the graves smoothed out and there was silence down below.

Miriam had heard about this but she did not want to believe it. — Riboinoi shel Oilom — she thought to herself, she must not lose her head, for she had two small children, Shloimele and Shmulik, and it was her duty to look after them. No, it could not be true that her children were orphans, that they no longer had a father. She trusted the Creator and went on believing that her husband would one day return.

But when there were no more men left, the nazis began to collect the children. They appeared every Tuesday, without fail, and they did not take many children at a time, just five or six. Nobody knew into which house they would break or which mother would be robbed of her children. The Biblical day of Ki Toiv was a black and accursed day to the Jewish mothers of Drohobyce.

What happened to these children abducted by the nazis? If they were twins, they were given chocolate and semolina in milk and arrived in excellent condition at Dr. Mengele's experimental camp. The sick were taken to isolation hospitals and used for experiments in vivisection; and the strong and the healthy were used in the training of bloodhounds.

Feverishly Miriam set to work. In one of the rooms, she uprooted the floor-boards, dug a large, deep pit, and plastered it with clay. The clever little boys understood what she was doing, for Shloimele had already studied the Gemore and little Shmulik always followed his brother's lead. When the accursed black Tuesday arrived, the two

children climbed quietly, without complaint, into
the pit under the floor.

But one Tuesday the Germans failed to put in
an appearance. Miriam waited. On the Wednesday
the poor children remained under the floor-boards
all day and all night. On Thursday morning the
Germans broke into the house.

"Where are your sons?"

"I don't know." Miriam replied, her whole body
trembling. "They left the house early and have not
returned yet."

"Search the house." the S.S. captain snarled and
his face was cold and cruel.

The nazi detachment knew its job. They tapped
the walls and floors with iron rods. Over the
children's hiding place the floor gave a hollow
sound. The nazis soon pulled the trembling, half
conscious little boys from the pit.
Miriam screamed, she thought she would lose her
mind. She threw herself on her knees before the S.S.
captain, begged, wept and held the two children
to her breast as if her arms had turned into iron
clamps. She screeched at the nazis like a wounded
tigress.

"I won't let you take my children, you won't take
them from me!"

The blue eyes of the captain glinted like steel. He reached for his camera and took a picture. He had quite a collection of pictures showing cowardly Jews for a documentary file he was making. The half-crazed, screaming Jewess with her madly dilated eyes and her two shaking, terrified Jewish brats made an excellent picture. He had a few interesting snapshots in his collection of running Jewish children pursued by the blood-hounds that had been set on them, the little boys' earlocks fluttering in the wind, like symbols of Jewish cowardice. Then he had pictures of bearded old Jews hanging from trees, their tongues lolling out amusingly. Wonderful caricatures for the Sturmer!

"All right," the captain said at long last, "I won't take both your brats, you can keep one. I give you five minutes to choose."

Miriam got to her feet. Her petrified mind began to work feverishly. Which should she choose? Shloimele had been the name of her deceased grandfather, he was his grandfather's heritage. Shmulik was the younger and the sweeter, but to her heart both were equally dear. The minutes fled with terrible speed. Miriam smoothed down her skirt with an involuntary movement, straightened the kerchief on her head and tied it more firmly

under her chin. As the minutes flew, a great re-
solution grew and crystallized in her heart.

The German officer counted the sixtieth second
of the fifth miunte on his stop-watch.

Miriam stood straight at him. She no longer
looked mad, she was not weeping, her eyes were
dry, she had suddenly grown above herself and
was now the real counterpart of the great prophet-
ess whose name she bore.

She said in a whisper but very calmly:
"I shall not choose!"

After the great catastrophe, the parlour-psycholo-
gists declared that there was no more cowardly na-
tion in the world than the ghetto-Jews. They walked
to the slaughterhouse without resistance, completely resigned, like a herd of sheep.

Only you know, you Jewish mothers, who survived the days of horror and are today bringing up
your children in freedom and hope for a better,
more beautiful future, how indescribably heroic
that Jewish mother, Miriam of Drohobyce had been
when she herself pronounced this new Solomonic
judgement over her sons.

ABOUT THE AUTHOR

M. D. Weinstock was born in Hungary 1922 and received both a Yehivah and higher secular education. Survived the Holocaust in a Forced Labour Camp, but lost most of his family to Nazi brutality. M. D. Weinstock was Editor and writer of several Orthodox Jewish papers in Hungarian from 1953-1979 (his wife Olga as coeditor of Uj Horizont) He wrote several books, articles and humorous parodies. In English translation: "Scandal in Brooklyn".
The author is currently working on two other books, near completion is: "Convert in the Holocaust" in which he describes his own experiences in the Forced Labour Camps and how he kept kosher with a few others all the time.
Currently Moshe David and Olga Weinstock own Bezalel Art, an Art Gallery, devoted to Jewish subjects only, with paintings, lithographs and rare prints, in N.Y.C.

EMMANUIL SNITKOVSKY, the illustrator of this book, is one of the outstanding artists, -emigrant from the USSR- whose paintings and graphics are shown in Bezalel Art-